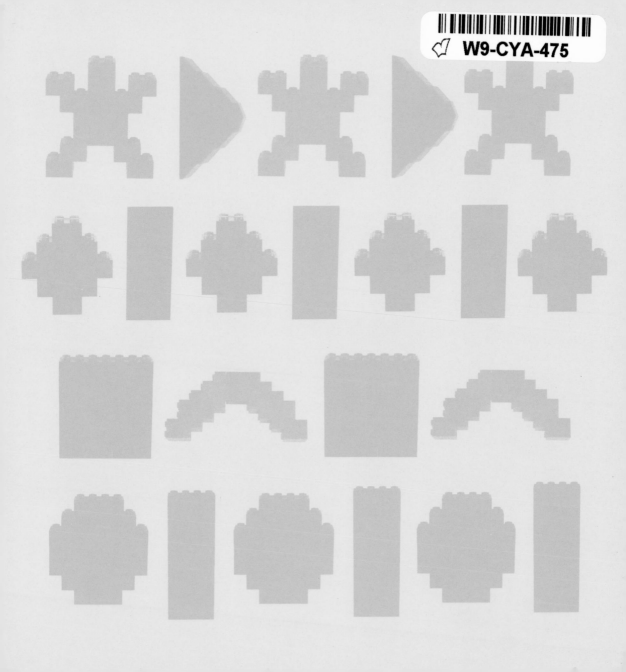

Brick by Brick

Colors

Sandy Creek
NEW YORK

Red

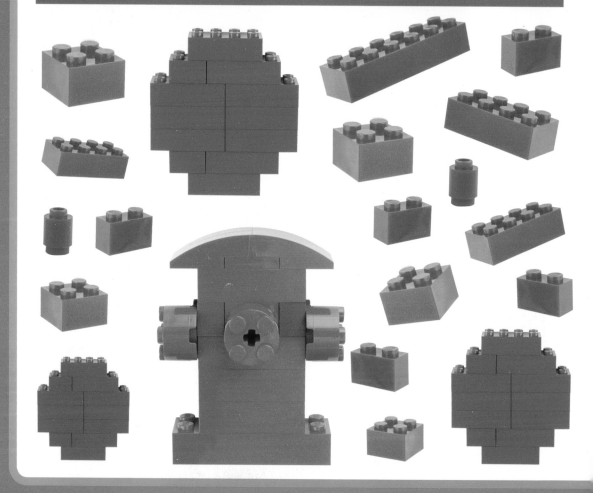

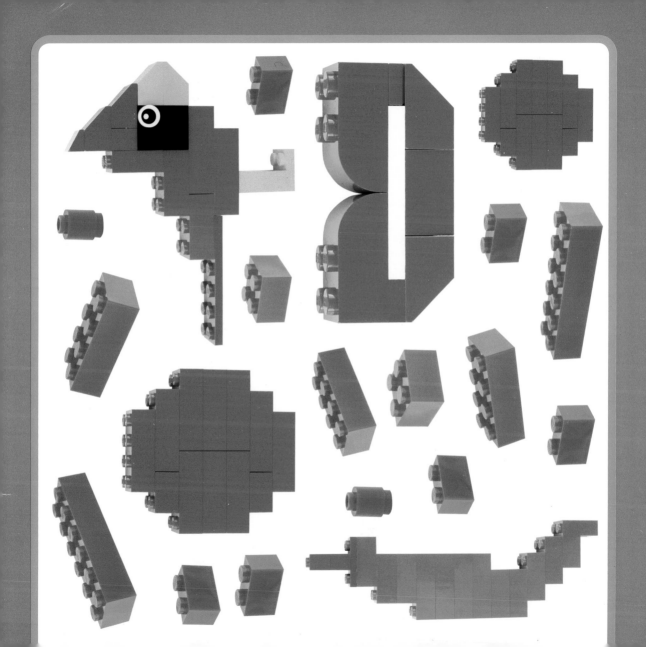

Fire hydrant

1×
4×
4×
3×
1×
3×
3×

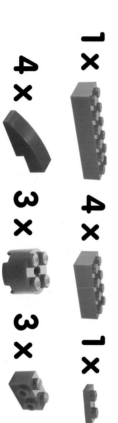

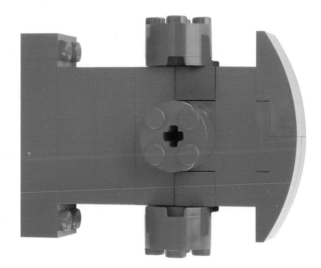

Lips

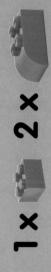

1× 2×

2× 2× 2×

Red bird

1x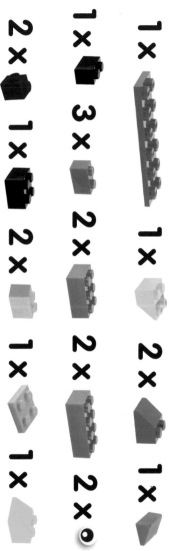

1x

1x

3x

1x

2x

2x

2x 2x

2x 2x

1x 1x

1x 2x

1x

1x

2x

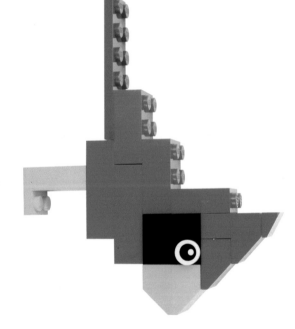

Chili pepper

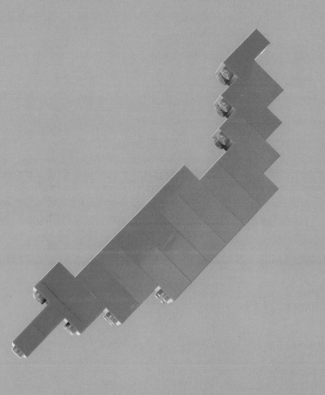

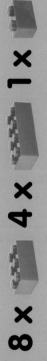

8 ×

4 ×

1 ×

2 ×

1 ×

Orange

4 ×

32 ×

16 ×

4 ×

4 ×

1 ×

Octopus

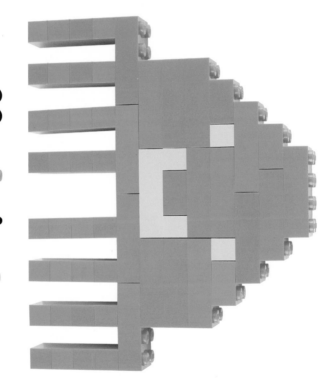

Fox

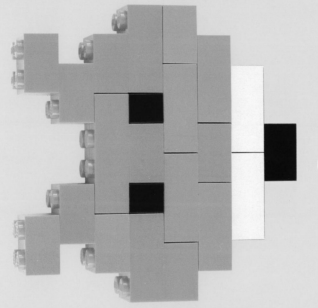

10 x   2 x

1 x   2 x

1 x   6 x

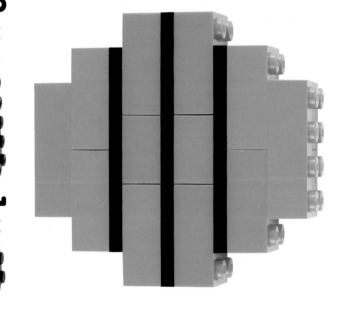

2 ×

3 ×

8 ×

1 ×

2 ×

Basketball

Carrot

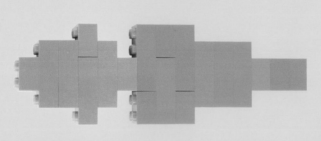

3 x

4 x

6 x

6 x

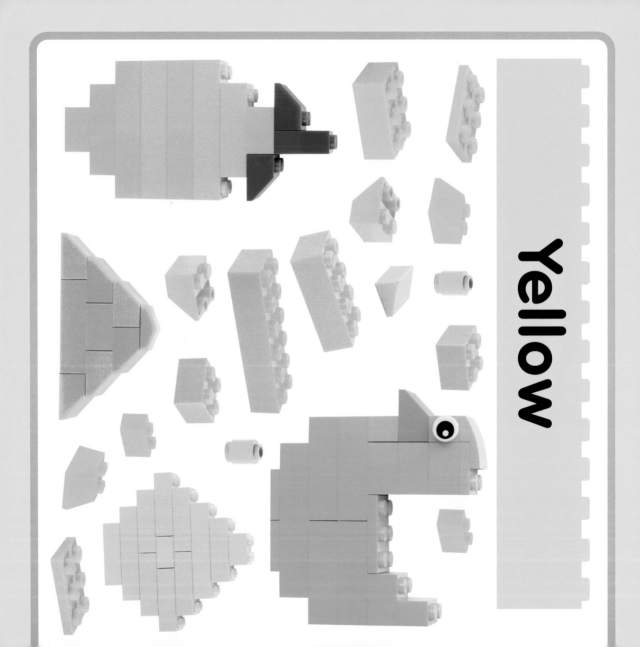

Yellow

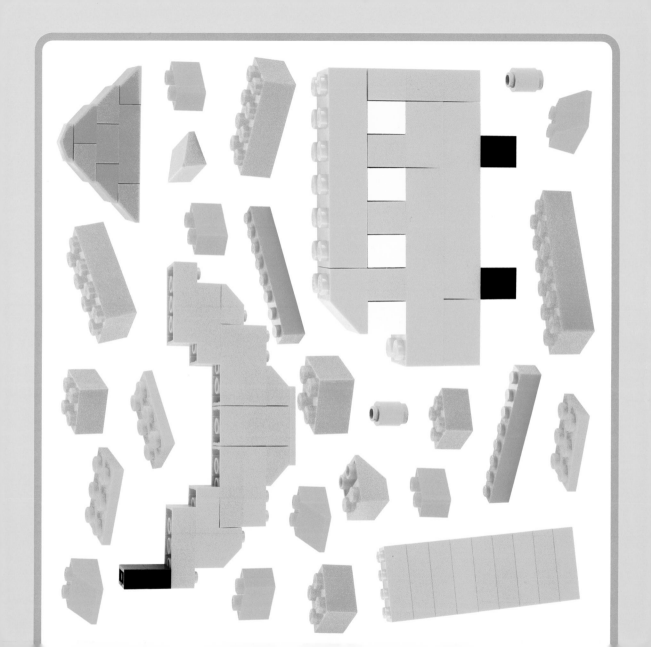

8 x

2 x 1 x

3 x

4 x

Banana

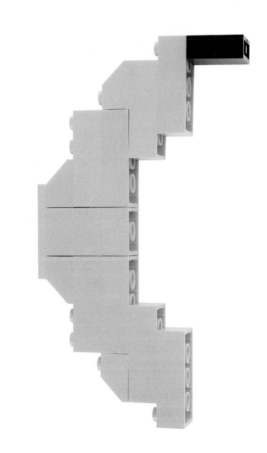

School bus

6 ×   3 ×   4 ×   2 ×   1 ×   2 ×

4x

1x

2x 2x

2x 1x

3x

4x

4x 1x

1x 2x

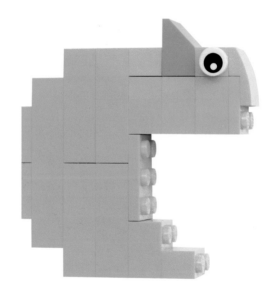

Lemon

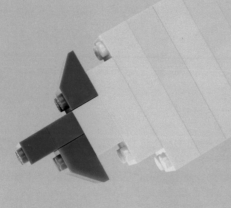

2× 2×

2×

2× 4×

2×

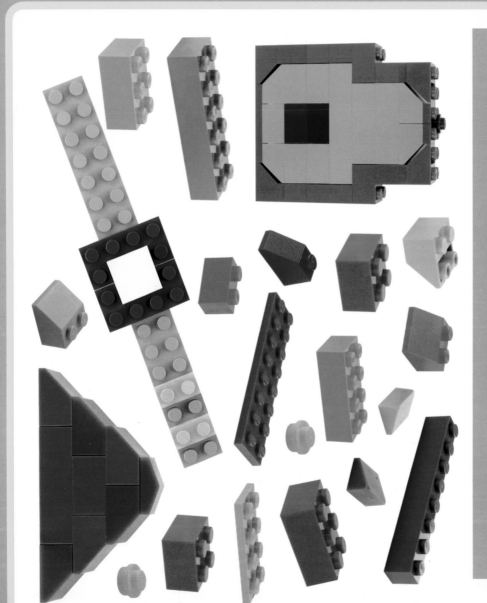

Green

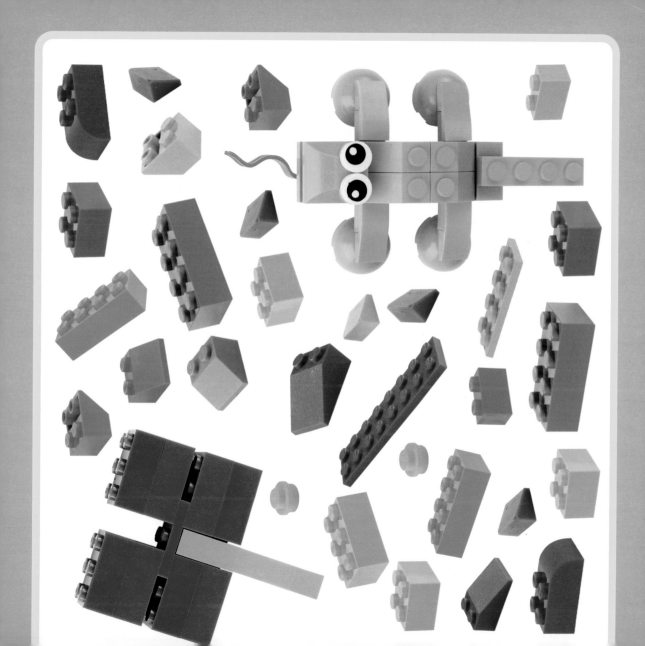

8 x

5 x

1 x

Clover

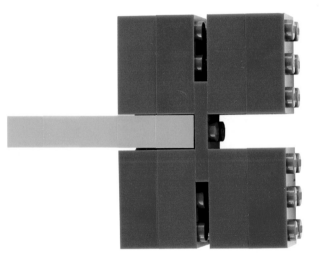

Watch

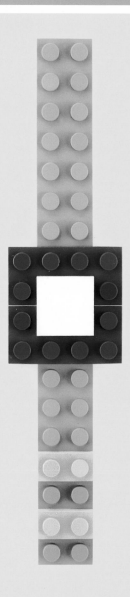

2 ×

2 × 2 × 1 ×

2 ×

Lizard

1×

1×

1×

1× 2×

2× 3×

4× 4× 4× 4×

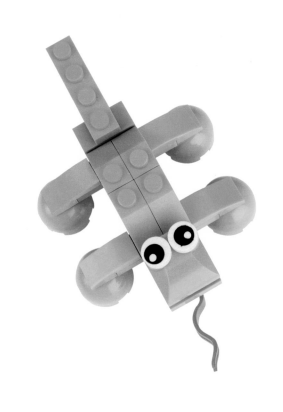

Avocado

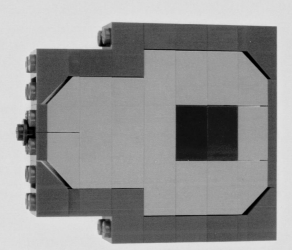

2 × 2 ×

2 × 2 ×

5 ×

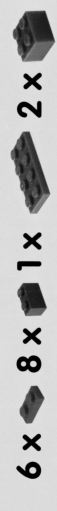

6 × 8 × 1 ×

2 × 2 × 1 ×

2 × 1 × 2 ×

Blue

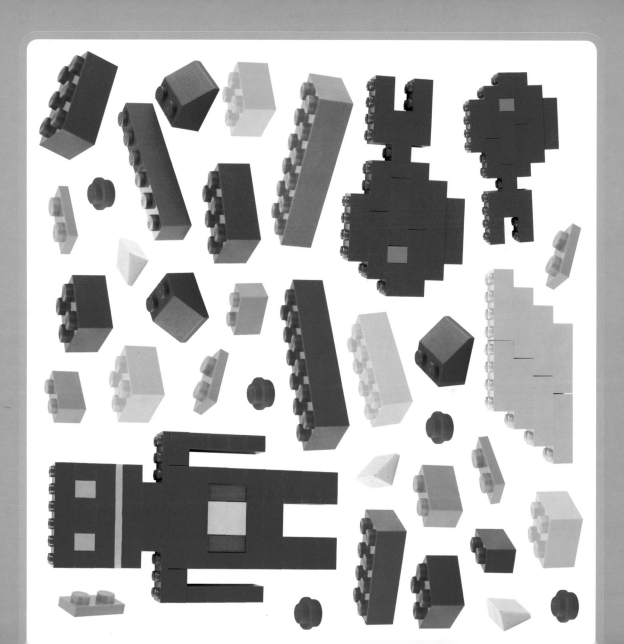

Robot

11 x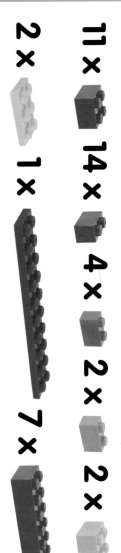

14 x

4 x

2 x

2 x

2 x

1 x

7 x

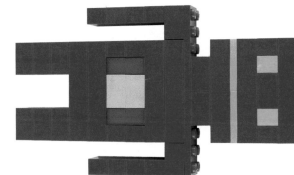

Fish

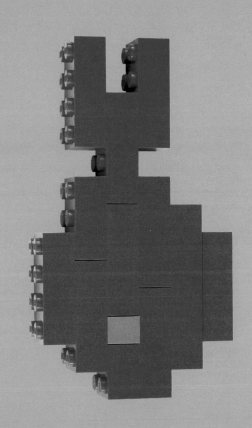

1×

9×

1×

1×

1×

1×

3× 13×

6× 5×

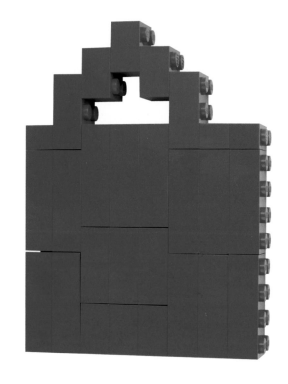

Mug

Jeans

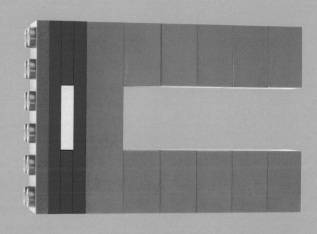

2 x

2 x

1 x

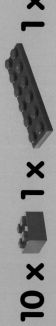

1 x

1 x

10 x

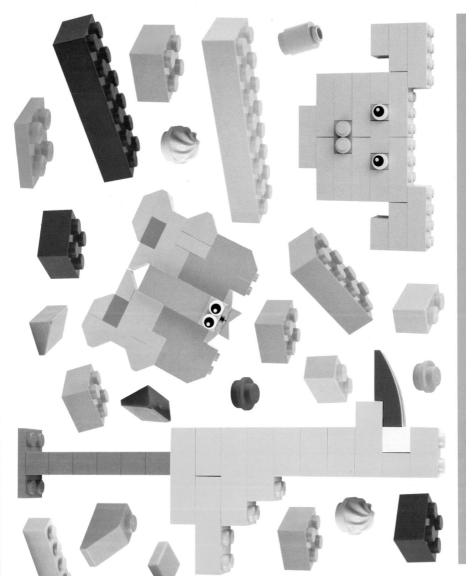

Pink and Purple

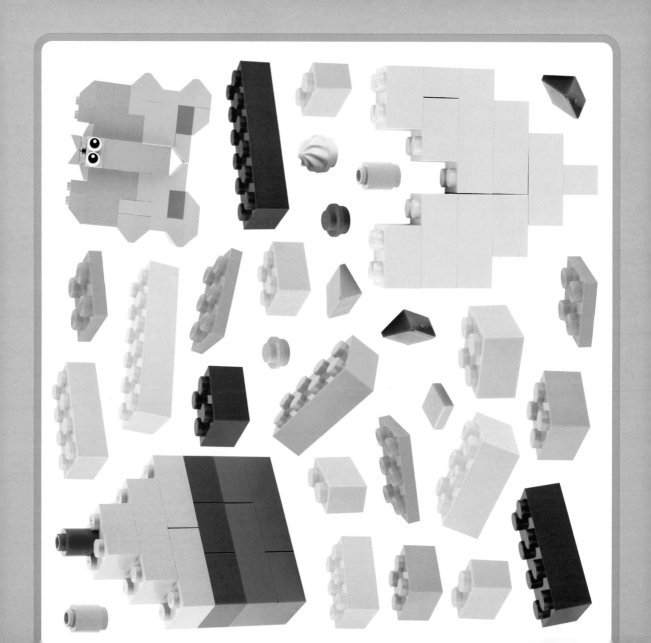

Flamingo

6 x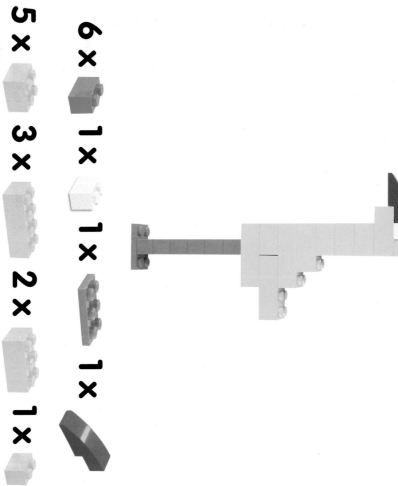

1 x

1 x

1 x

1 x

5 x

3 x

2 x

1 x

Cupcake

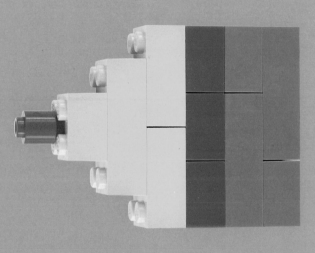

1x 2x 2x 1x

1x 1x 2x 3x

Butterfly

2×
2×
2×
2×
2×
2× 2×
2× 4×
2× 4×
2× 6× 1×
2× 6× 2×
4× 6× 4×
4× 2× 2×
2× 2×

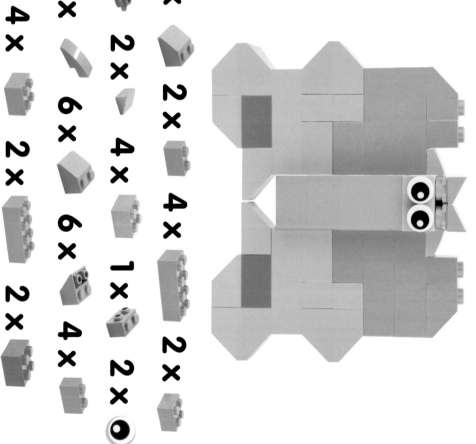

Pig

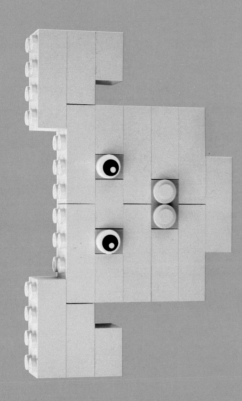

5x 9x 4x 2x

1x 2x 2x 2x

Brown

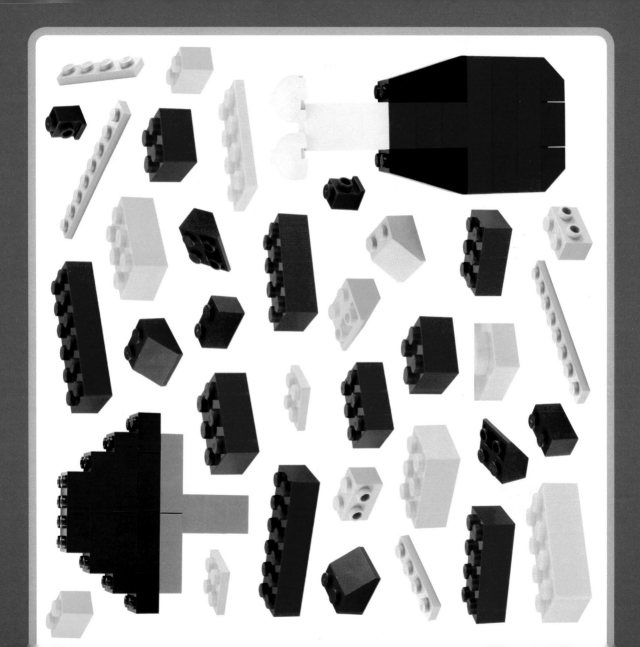

3 ×
3 × 2 ×
2 × 2 ×
2 ×

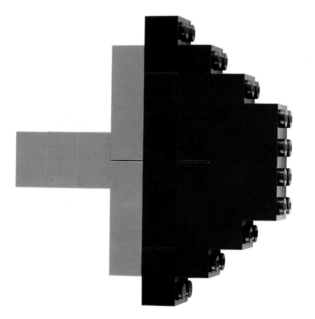

Mushroom

Bear

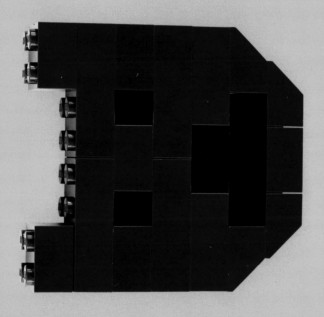

6 × 1 × 2 ×

4 × 2 × 4 × 1 ×

6 × 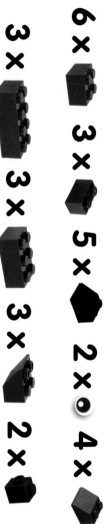 3 × 5 × 2 × 4 ×

3 × 3 × 3 × 3 × 3 × 2 ×

Horse

Turkey leg

2 ×

2 ×

2 ×

2 ×

3 ×

3 ×

4 ×

Gray

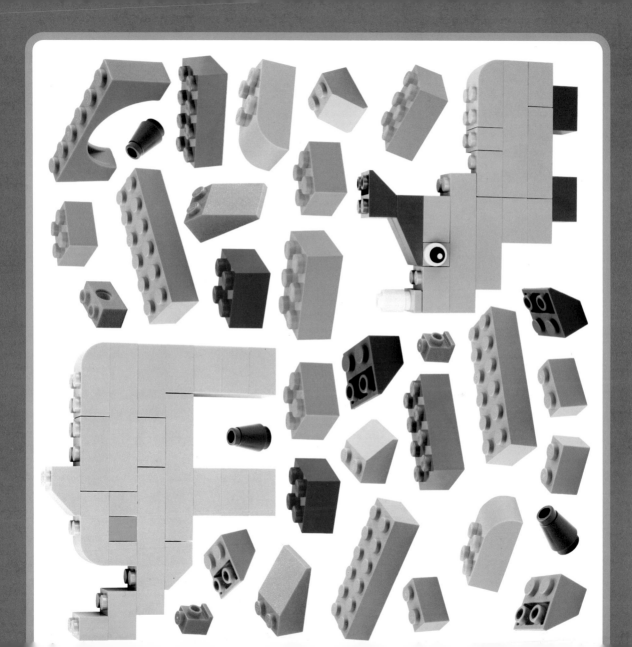

1× 3× 1× 2×

2× 9× 1× 3×

Elephant

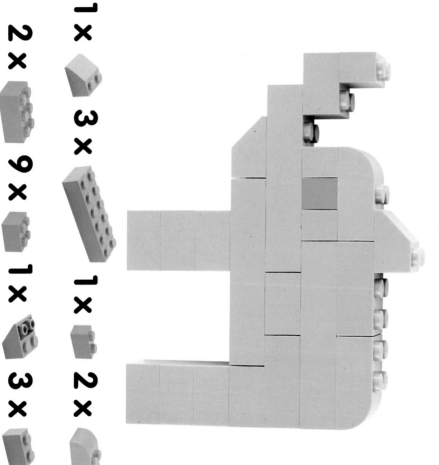

Hammer

8×

1×

1×

2×

4×

2×

2×

2×

3×

1×

4×

1×

2×

4×

5×

1×

5×

1×

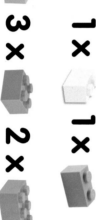

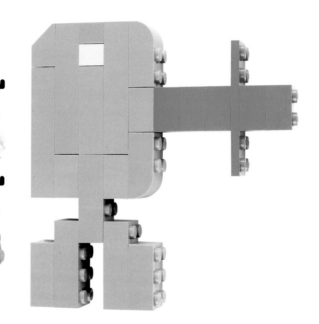

Whale

Rhino

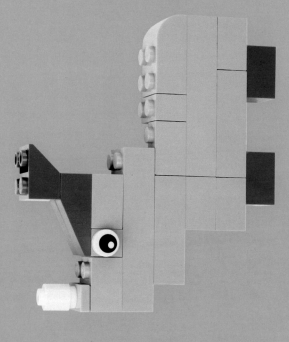

2 ×   2 ×   1 ×

1 ×   2 ×   2 ×

2 ×   6 ×   1 ×

1 ×   1 ×

1 ×   1 ×

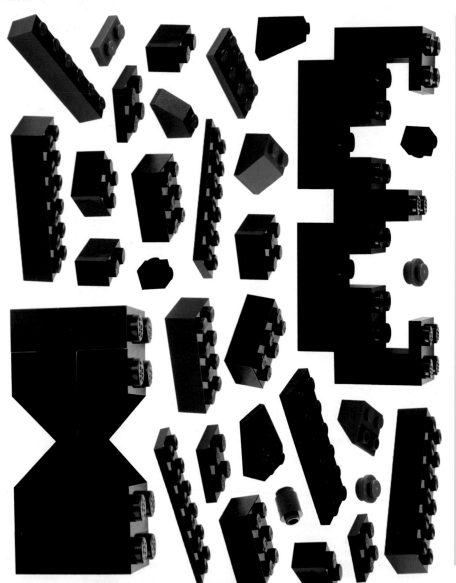

Black

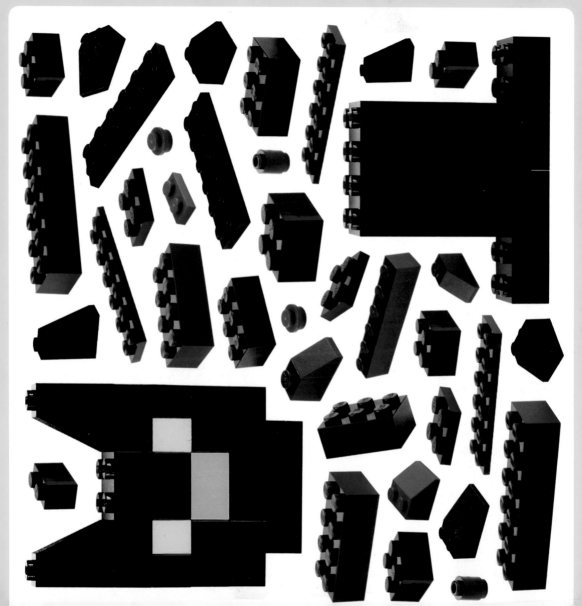

Cat

5 ×
3 ×
1 ×
2 ×
2 ×
2 ×

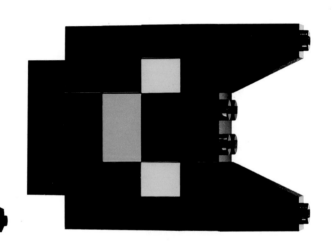

Mustache

2 x 3 x 3 x 2 x

6 x

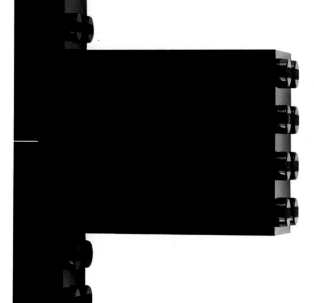

Top hat

Bow tie

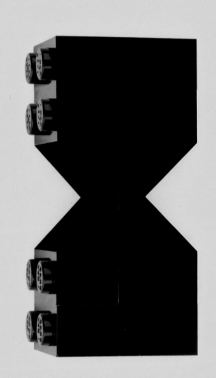

1x

4x

2x

2x

2x

An Imprint of Sterling Publishing Co., Inc.
1166 Avenue of the Americas
New York, NY 10036

SANDY CREEK and the distinctive Sandy Creek logo are registered trademarks
of Barnes & Noble, Inc.

Copyright © 2016 Weldon Owen Limited

ISBN 978-1-4351-6409-3

Manufactured in Guangdong, China.
Lot#:
2 4 6 8 10 9 7 5 3 1
08/16

www.sterlingpublishing.com